Fred
the Fire Truck

Written and Illustrated by Read With You
Center for Excellence in STEAM Education

Read With You

Published by Read With You Publishing. Printed in the United States of America.

Read With You and associated logos are trademarks and/or registered trademarks of Read With You L.L.C.

ISBN-13: 979-8-88618-053-4

First Edition March 2022

Red, white! Red, white!
What are those flashing lights?

2

Wee-woo! Wee-woo!
What is that loud sound?

3

Honk! Honk!
What is that HUGE honk?

It's Fred the fire truck!
Who is he helping today?

Fred pulls up to a house.
Oh, dear! There is smoke and fire!

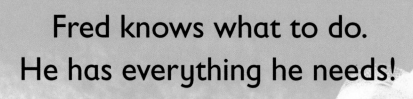

Fred knows what to do.
He has everything he needs!

First, Fred is connected to the fire hydrant.

Then, the firefighter points the fire hose.

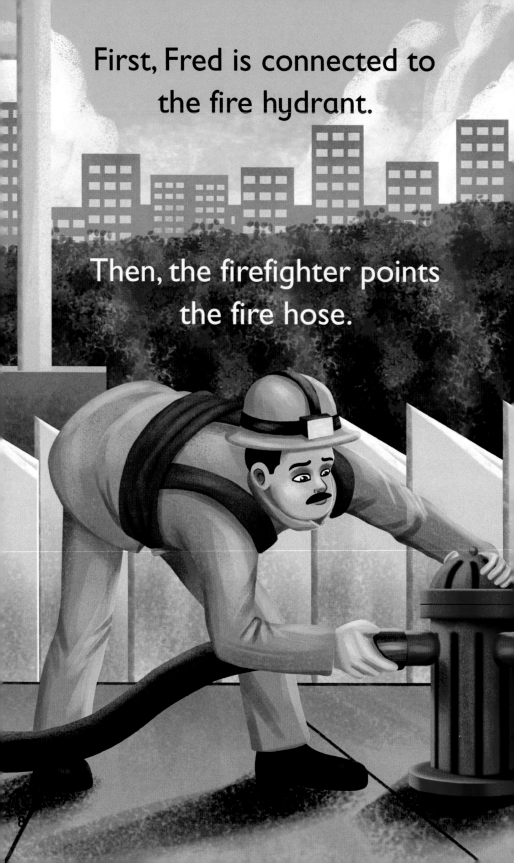

Whoosh! goes the water.
It shoots through the air!
Take that, fire.

"Help!" someone shouts.
Fred can help them, too.

He reaches out his biggest ladder.
He sends his bravest firefighters.

Everyone is safe.
Fred can relax, too.

Oh, wait! Not yet!
"Fred, we need your help!" calls
Fred's intercom.
"I'm on my way!" Fred responds.

Turn on your siren, Fred!
Wee-woo!   Wee-woo!
Let's go!

Fred arrives.
But, where is the smoke?
And, where are the flames?

Fred is puzzled.
Meow!
What's that? Fires do not meow!

"Fred, help!" a woman calls.
"My cat is stuck in the tree!"
Fred loves to help.
He has everything he needs!

First, Fred is connected to
the fire hydrant.
Then, the firefighter points
the fire hose.

Whoosh! *Hiss!*
Oh, dear.
That did not help.

19

It's okay!
He has an ax!
Chop, chop!
Hiss!

Oh, dear.
That *also* did not help.
Maybe the ladder?

Hooray! Kitty is safe.
Now, Fred can relax.

Fred slowly drives home.
His ladder is folded away.
His hose is wrapped up.

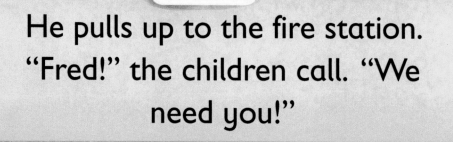

He pulls up to the fire station.
"Fred!" the children call. "We
need you!"

Oh, dear. Is it a fire?
Is there a cat in a tree? Or, a dog
in a river?

"We're hot," the children say.
"Can you spray your water?"

Fred laughs.
He shoots his water cannon and
the children run under it.

Fred is a fire truck.
He saves people and animals
every day.

Learner's Guide

Explore

Practice 1: Questions
Choose the correct answer.

Fred

1. Fred's lights are _____ .
   a. blue and yellow
   b. black and white
   c. red and white

2. Fred reaches out his long _____ .
   a. ladder
   b. ax
   c. siren

3. Firefighters can use an _____ to get through a door.
   a. ladder
   b. ax
   c. siren

4. Fred's hose connects to the _____ .
   a. fire hydrant
   b. siren
   c. ladder

5. Fred's _____ sprays water.
   a. ax
   b. cat
   c. hose

Practice 2: Vocabulary

Read each word below. Can you find each one on a fire truck? Write a check mark next to the objects you can find on a fire truck.

Words	
____ ax	____ fire hydrant
____ firefighter	____ bandage
____ heart monitor	____ horn
____ siren	____ ladder
____ hose	____ stretcher

 **Connect**

Practice 1: Questions

- Have you ever seen a fire truck on your street? If yes, why was it there?

- Where is the closest fire station to your house?

- What are some ways to stay safe from a fire?

- Do you know where the fire exits are in your house? Ask an adult!

- What does a firefighter do?

Practice 2: Visit

Ask an adult if you can visit your local fire station! See how long it takes to walk or drive there. How many fire trucks are at the station? How many firefighters work there? Thank the firefighters for the work they do in keeping your community safe!

 # Craft

Let's get crafty! Find a separate sheet of paper and a pen. Copy the steps below to draw Fred the fire truck.

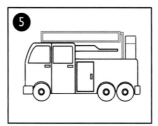
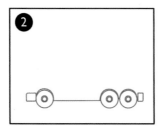
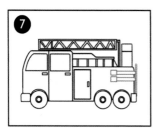
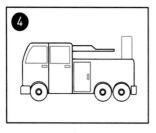
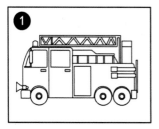
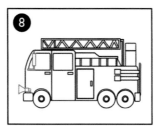

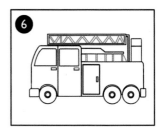
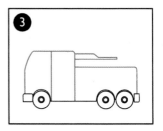

Made in the USA
Columbia, SC
09 October 2022